WHO LIVES WITH YOU?

By Barbara S. Cain and Sherry L. Hatcher

Illustrated by Ruth Van Sciver

YOUTH PUBLICATIONS / THE SATURDAY EVENING POST COMPANY

3

INTRODUCTION

Throughout the ages, man has asked the eternal question, Who Am I? The question may never be truly answered, but it is imperative that all of us seek a solution that will make us comfortable with our everyday lives.

Children, too, seek the answer to this question. In this complex world where technology and science seem to have the answers to most problems, great attention must be given to youngsters who are trying to find their places in society. It is not easy to find a place to "belong." It depends upon many things—intelligence, heredity, economic circumstances, and level of education. But it also depends upon a cheerful outlook and self-determination.

And of course, every child must feel wanted and needed. In this respect, children are no different from adults. It is also universally recognized that a good solid start in school influences later decisions a great deal. That is why it is important to make the young child feel good about himself and his world.

As the family becomes a less stable influence in our society, it is important for the young child to feel secure with his own family structure, no matter how different from the norm. This problem has not always been addressed adequately in our classrooms.

Now, this delightful volume of "shapes" provides an immediate opportunity to delve into a child's feelings about his own background—a mini-piece of anthropology for the young child.

And how delightfully it presents an answer for even the most inquisitive child. Why does Johnny not live with his mother? Why does Susie live with her aunt and uncle? How can a child possibly be happy if he doesn't live with *either* of his parents? The answers to these questions and many more are presented in a sensitive and pleasing manner. How much fun each child will have thinking about the "shape" of his own family structure! Children will learn about themselves and about each other. They will learn about the family unit in all possible shapes and forms. Tolerance and understanding will come as a natural result.

This book is an excellent way for children to become acquainted with one another and presents its lessons with humor and understanding. It also represents various ethnic groups, along with possible family molds. The *adopted* family, the *extended* family, even the *commune* family will show children the family in its infinite variety—family variations the child either lives within or beside.

There is no attempt to editorialize or preach. The subject matter is treated almost tenderly, and succeeds admirably in not offending anyone. This book should provide a normalizing effect and influence on the ever-increasing number of children living in atypical family structures.

Children seek to feel comfortable with one another. With the lessons learned in this collection of various "shapes," youngsters may discover how many answers there are to the question, Who Am I? But most importantly, they will learn there is no *single* answer; each must find the answer that suits him. *Who Lives With You?* is a delightful way to encourage boys and girls to be aware of the many differences in families. But it is also a practical, yet intelligent approach to an increasing awareness of the importance of giving children a feeling of security within their own circumstances.

It was a special day for Sally.

She wore her favorite blue-green shirt to school that day.

She brought Loopy, her favorite stuffed animal, to school.

She even let her friend Jessie play with Loopy.

"It must be a special day for you, Sally," Jessie said. "You NEVER let me play with Loopy."

"It IS a special day," Sally said. "Today my grandma is coming to live with us. Soon I'll be living with

my mommy,

my daddy,

and my grandma, too."

"Who lives with you, Jessie?" Sally asked.

"I live with my mom

and my dad

and my bossy big brother," Jessie said.

Lots of children heard the girls talking. They began asking one another, "Who lives with YOU?"

Soon it became a game.

The children named the game "Who Lives With You?"

Kenny was the first to tell.

"I live with my mom,

my dad,

and my new baby sister.

She has no teeth!"

The teacher drew a picture of everyone who lives with Kenny.

MOM

DAD

KEN

SIS

"Different families come in different shapes," the teacher said.
She drew some lines joining everyone who lives with Kenny.

"I get it," Kenny said. "My family is shaped like a square."

"Now do me! Now do my family!" Marcy cried, bouncing up and down like a beach ball.

"Who lives with you?" Sally asked.

"I live with my mom and my brother," Marcy answered.

"Your family looks like a triangle," Sally said.

"That's right!" Marcy said. "My family looks just like a three-cornered hat."

"We used to look like a triangle, too," Tim and Terry said. "Now our family is a different shape."

"Who lives with you?" Sally asked.

"Well, we used to live with just our dad," the boys answered.

"And Sara and Sue used to live with just their mom."

"Then our triangle joined their triangle."

"And NOW we're all a brand-new shape!"

"That looks like a trapezoid," Sally said proudly.

"A trap-a-what?" Kenny asked.

"A trapezoid, silly."

"What's a trapezoid?" Kenny wanted to know.

"It's what THEY are." Sally grinned, and pointed to the drawing of Terry and Tim's family.

Tony was playing on the jungle gym.

He was twisted up like a pretzel.

"My family changed its shape, too," he said.

"Who lives with you?" Sally asked.

"I used to live with just my mom and dad," Tony replied.

"You looked like an ice-cream cone without the ice cream,"
Sally laughed.

"Then we adopted my little brother," Tony added.

"Now you're a square shape, just like us," said Kenny.

"I bet you can't guess MY shape," Stevie said, hiding inside a spaceship.

"Who lives with you?" Sally asked.

"I live with old people and new people—
  big people and little people.
  I live with my parents, and grandparents,
  my aunt and uncle, and my cousins, too.
I live with FOURTEEN other people in the very same house."

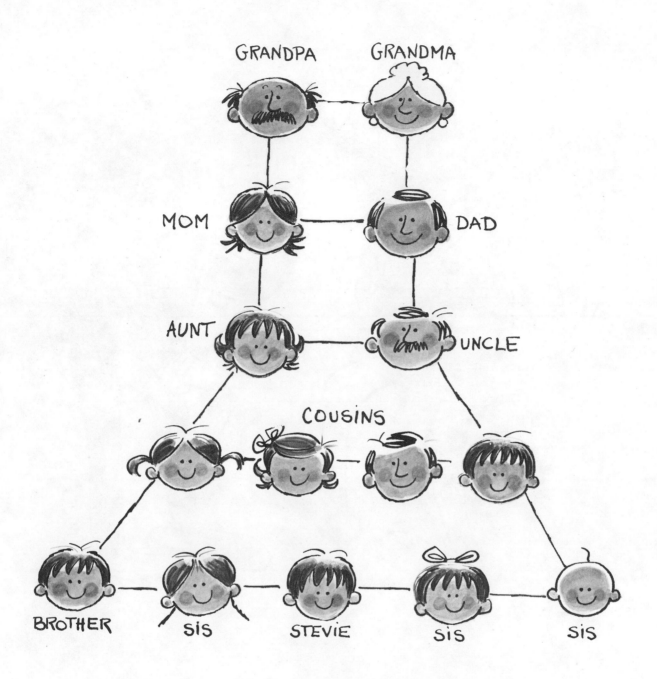

"You look like a beach hat!" Marcy said.

"A ballerina's skirt!" Jessie giggled.

"A sand castle!" Kenny added.

"My shape is different from EVERYBODY'S," Lucy declared.
"I'm one shape in the morning and another at night."
"Who lives with you?" Sally asked.
"In the mornings, I live with eight other children in my day-care house," Lucy answered.

"You look like a string of beads," Sally said.

"And at the end of the day—I live with my mom when she comes home from work," Lucy said.

MOM

LUCY

"Then you're a number eight," Tim said.

"A snowman," Stevie insisted.

"You'll never guess my shape," Laurie said. "I know you won't guess!"

"Then who lives with you?" the children asked.

"I live with my family and seven other families in the same big house," said Laurie.

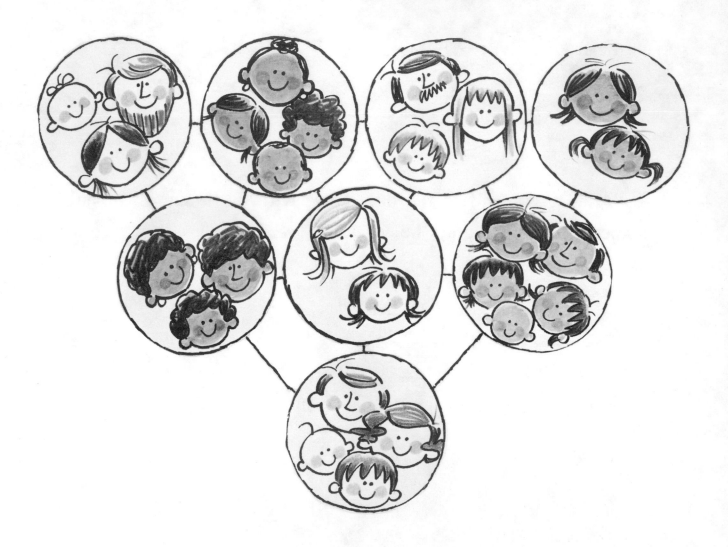

"You all look like a bunch of grapes," Sally teased.

"See, we CAN guess your shape."

"Wait till you hear about my family," Chuckie said.

"Who lives with you?" the children asked.

"I live with my aunt and three spices."

"THREE SPICES?" the children shouted.

"Yup," Chuckie said with a twinkle in his eyes.

"There's Aunt Molly and me and three pups named Cinnamon, Pepper, and Ginger."

"Your family looks like the letter *L* ," Timmy said.

"A number *7*," Terry said.

"A number *7* IF you're standing on your head!" Timmy laughed.

As the teacher drew more family shapes, some of the children made their own.

Chuckie built one out of tinker toys.

Bruce built another with blocks.

Julie was playing in the storybook corner.
She did a cutout of Snow White and the Seven Dwarfs,

and Goldilocks and the Three Bears.

After everybody played "Who Lives With You?" the teacher spread all the pictures across the floor.

The children could see all kinds of families. . .
All kinds of sizes. . .
All kinds of shapes. . .
All kinds of shades. . .

The children could see that

Whatever the size. . .

Whatever the shape. . .

Whatever the shade. . .

EVERYBODY lives with SOMEONE.

WHO LIVES WITH YOU?

GRANDMOTHER   MOTHER   FATHER   GRANDFATHER

AUNT   UNCLE   SISTER   BROTHER

COUSIN   STEPMOTHER   STEPFATHER

BABY   FRIEND

WHO LIVES WITH YOU?

You may use these pages to draw pictures and play the game
"Who Lives With You?"